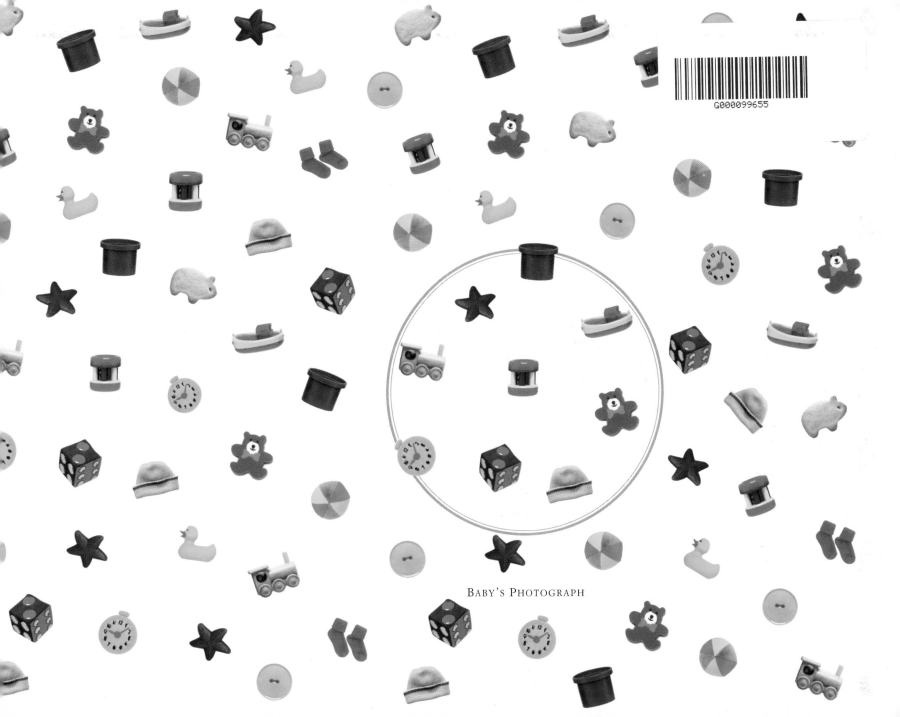

BABY'S PHOTOGRAPH

MILLENNIUM
Baby
RECORD
BOOK

CONTENTS

DORLING KINDERSLEY

London • New York • Sydney • Moscow

www.dk.com

Millennium Baby

❧

To you, the birth of your baby is one of the most significant events of your life, whatever the date. The emotions a new baby triggers are timeless.

Some of those emotions centre on the symbolic nature of birth. A baby marks a new beginning in a family's history and becomes the focus for many of its members' hopes, or even fears. In each one of us, our sense of what the future may hold is shaped by the ever-changing environment we grew up in. We hope for "better" futures, while trying to hang on to the meaningful experiences of our pasts; a new baby is a focus for our hopes and for our optimism. Recording the first events of your baby's life and keeping a memento, such as a lock of hair, are like rites of passage, helping you to preserve something of your child as he or she grows and changes. Each memento is like a small trophy and each milestone is a sign of progress.

**So what is different about a baby born at the
start of a new millennium? And why celebrate
a millennium baby in particular?**

At no time are we so symbolically perched on the brink of the
"future" than at the start of a new millennium. So, inevitably,
millennium babies will be seen as historical markers – as starters
in the line-up for the expedition into an unfolding age. At no
time in the past has a generation been so scrutinised as the new
millennium generation is likely to be. It may even be a generation
seen to encapsulate all that is good and all that is questionable
about the progress of human society. On a personal level, for you
and your family, a millennium birth will be a reference point. This
record book will be the mini "time-capsule" that celebrates that
start; it will be preserved for posterity and, most importantly,
preserved for your millennium baby as he or she grows up.

—Baby's Arrival—

Baby's name
....

Date of birth
....

Place of birth
....

Day of birth
....

Time of birth
....

BIRTH MAY BE A MATTER OF A MOMENT.
BUT IT IS A UNIQUE ONE.
Frédérick Leboyer

Present at birth
....

Monday's child is fair of face,
Tuesday's child is full of grace,
Wednesday's child is full of woe,
Thursday's child has far to go,
Friday's child is loving and giving,
Saturday's child works hard for a living,
And the child that is born on the Sabbath day
Is bonny and blithe, and good and gay.

HOROSCOPE

Zodiac sign
....

Chinese horoscope
....

Birthstone
....

Flower

Weight at birth

....

Length at birth

....

Colour of eyes

....

Colour of hair

....

Circumference of head

....

Description of the birth

....

....

Birth cards received

BIRTH ANNOUNCEMENT

FIRST DAYS

First visitors

Their comments

Feeding schedule

Baby's feeding times

Duration of each feed

Description of a feed

Sleeping schedule

Sleeping times

Wakeful times

Favourite sleeping position

Mother's feelings

Father's feelings

A BABE IS FED WITH MILK AND PRAISE.

Charles and Mary Lamb

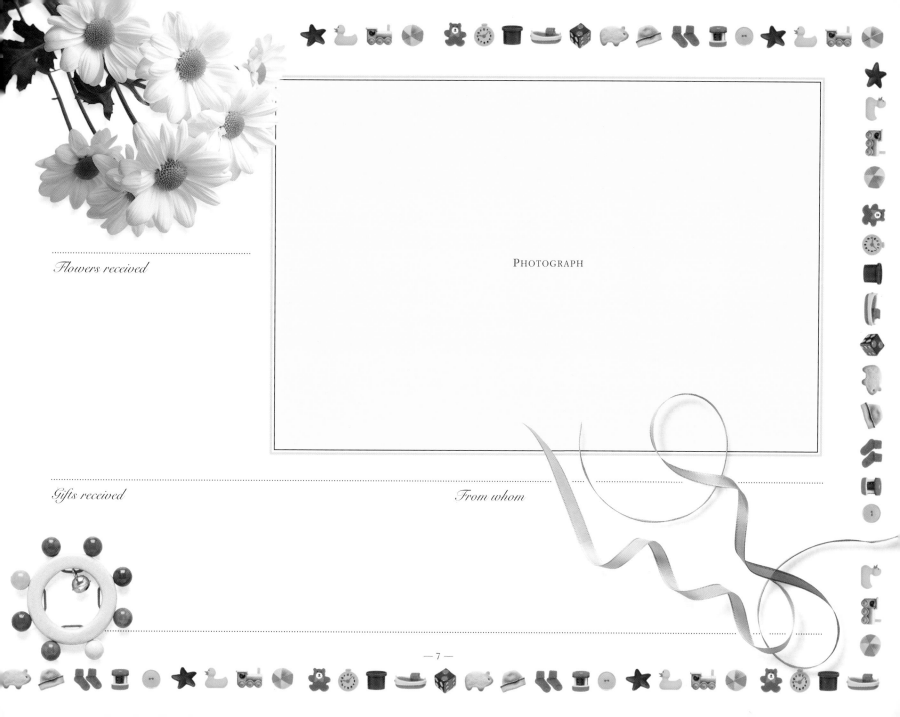

Flowers received

PHOTOGRAPH

Gifts received   From whom

Name Ceremony

INVITATION

Gifts received

Your baby's behaviour

Reason for choosing name

Description of ceremony

Your baby's outfit

Giving a name is indeed a poetic art.

Thomas Carlyle

Guests attending

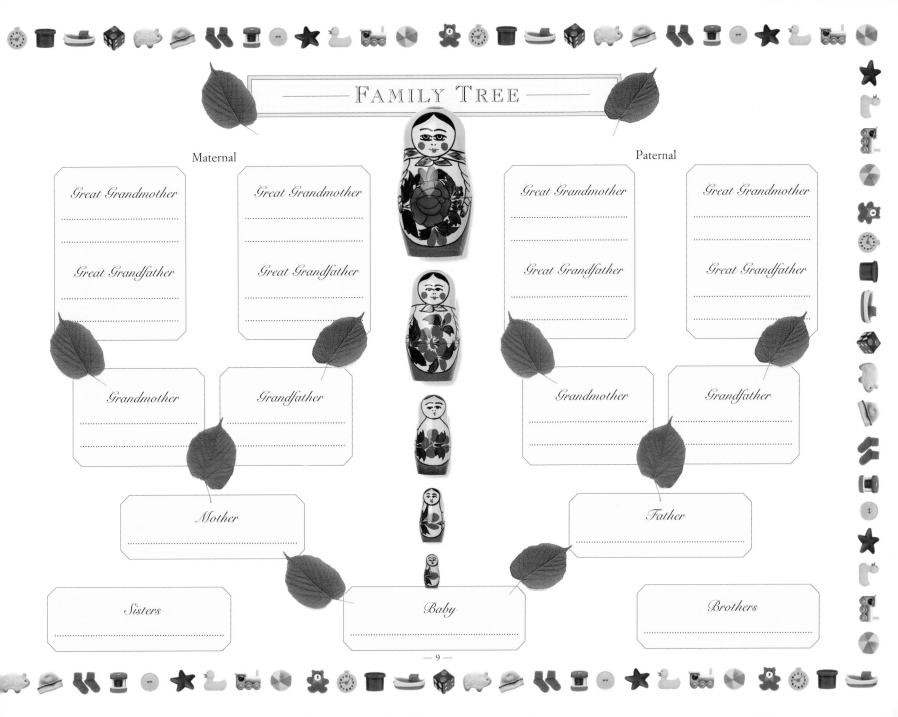

FAMILY TREE

Maternal

Paternal

Great Grandmother
....
....

Great Grandfather
....
....

Great Grandmother
....
....

Great Grandfather
....
....

Great Grandmother
....
....

Great Grandfather
....
....

Great Grandmother
....
....

Great Grandfather
....
....

Grandmother
....
....

Grandfather
....
....

Grandmother
....
....

Grandfather
....
....

Mother
....

Father
....

Sisters
....

Baby
....

Brothers
....

FIRST FOODS

Most babies are introduced to solid foods at between three and six months old, and will relish discovering new tastes and textures.

THIS WOULD BE A BETTER WORLD FOR CHILDREN IF PARENTS HAD TO EAT THE SPINACH.

Groucho Marx

*Little Miss Muffet sat on a tuffet
Eating her curds and whey.
Along came a spider, and sat down beside her
And frightened Miss Muffet away.*

Date your baby first:

Ate puréed food

Ate solid food

Ate with a spoon

Ate in a high chair

Drank from a cup

*The Queen of Hearts, she made some tarts,
All on a summer day;
The Knave of Hearts, he stole those tarts,
And took them quite away!*

Favourite food

Description of a meal

Date of final feed from breast or bottle

TEETHING

ADAM AND EVE HAD MANY ADVANTAGES, BUT THE PRINCIPAL ONE WAS THAT THEY ESCAPED TEETHING.

Mark Twain

A baby cuts 20 primary or milk teeth, which begin to be replaced with permanent teeth when the child is about six years old. The appearance of the first tooth is a milestone in a baby's life, although it can cause a great deal of discomfort. Some babies find chewing on a teething ring soothes the gums and helps lessen the pain.

Date of first tooth

Date of second tooth

Date of third tooth

Date of fourth tooth

Date of fifth tooth

Teething symptoms

Notes

Top teeth

Teething order

Bottom teeth

2
3   3
7   7
5   5
10   10
9   9
6   6
8   8
4   4
1

PEOPLE WHO SAY THEY SLEEP LIKE A BABY USUALLY DON'T HAVE ONE.

Leo J. Burke

Bedtime
....

Wakes at
....

Favourite sleeping position
....

Bedtime comforters
....

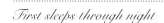

First sleeps through night
....

First sleeps in cot
....

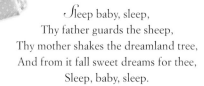

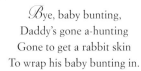

*Bye, baby bunting,
Daddy's gone a-hunting
Gone to get a rabbit skin
To wrap his baby bunting in.*

*Sleep baby, sleep,
Thy father guards the sheep,
Thy mother shakes the dreamland tree,
And from it fall sweet dreams for thee,
Sleep, baby, sleep.*

Description of cot

Description of nursery

Notes

> HE SMILES AND CLASPS HIS TINY HAND
> WITH SUNBEAMS O'ER HIM GLEANING,
> A WORLD OF BABY FAIRYLAND
> HE VISITS WHILE HE'S DREAMING.
>
> Joseph Ashby-Sterry

Favourite lullabies

Favourite bed time toys

> Golden slumbers kiss your eyes;
> Smiles awake you when you rise;
> Sleep, pretty baby, do not cry,
> And I will sing you a lullaby.

FAVOURITE THINGS

Your baby's favourite:

....

Mobile

THE CHILDHOOD SHOWS THE MAN, AS MORNING
SHOWS THE DAY.

John Milton

....

Toys

....

Pictures

....

Books

....

Cuddly toys

....

Objects

—14—

Games

Activities

Sounds

Words

People

Animals

Stories

Songs and Nursery Rhymes

Hey diddle diddle
The cat and the fiddle,
The cow jumped over the moon;
The little dog laughed
To see such sport,
And the dish ran away with the spoon.

─Bathtime and Water Play─

First enjoys bath

....

First time in a big bath

....

Response to being bathed

....

Response to hair being washed

....

I'M VERY FOND OF WATER;
IT EVER MUST DELIGHT
EACH MOTHER'S SON AND DAUGHTER,
WHEN QUALIFIED ARIGHT.

Charles Neaves

Favourite bath toys

....

Bath time activities

....

Row, row, row your boat
Gently down the stream
Merrily, merrily, merrily, merrily,
Life is but a dream.

One, two, three, four, five,
Once I caught a fish alive,
Six, seven, eight, nine, ten,
Then I let him go again.
Why did you let him go?
Because he bit my finger so.
Which finger did he bite?
This little finger on the right.

First water play in garden

First play in paddling pool

First swim in swimming pool

Your baby's swimwear

PHOTOGRAPH

Favourite water games

FIRST CHRISTMAS

At Christmas play and make good cheer,
For Christmas comes but once a year.

Thomas Tusser

Christmas Day:

Where it was spent

Who it was spent with

Your present to your baby

Stocking gifts

Gifts received

From whom

Description of Christmas Day

Boxing Day:

Where it was spent

Who it was spent with

Description of Boxing Day

Favourite Christmas presents

Family Christmas activities

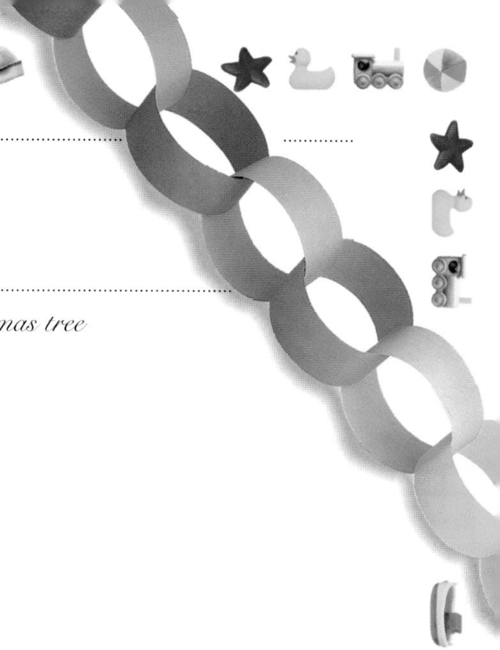

Favourite Christmas games

Description of the Christmas tree

PHOTOGRAPH

Christmas weather

Notes

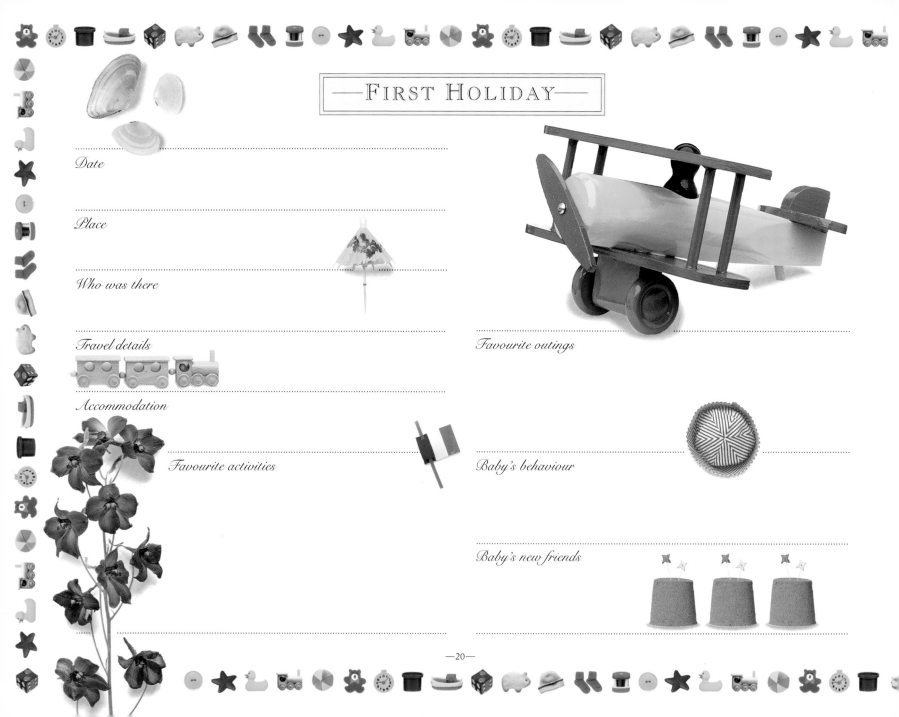

FIRST HOLIDAY

Date

Place

Who was there

Travel details

Accommodation

Favourite activities

Favourite outings

Baby's behaviour

Baby's new friends

—20—

PHOTOGRAPH

IT IS A HAPPY TALENT TO KNOW HOW TO PLAY.

Ralph Waldo Emerson

Favourite memories of the holiday

FIRST BIRTHDAY

Date ....

Description of cake ....

How celebrated ....

Your baby's outfit ....

Who was there ....

Gifts received ....

A HAPPY CHILDHOOD CAN'T BE
CURED. MINE'LL HANG AROUND
MY NECK LIKE A RAINBOW.

Hortense Calisher

Your present ....

Your baby's behaviour

*H*appy birthday to you
Happy birthday to you
Happy birthday dear baby
Happy birthday to you.

PHOTOGRAPH

Notes

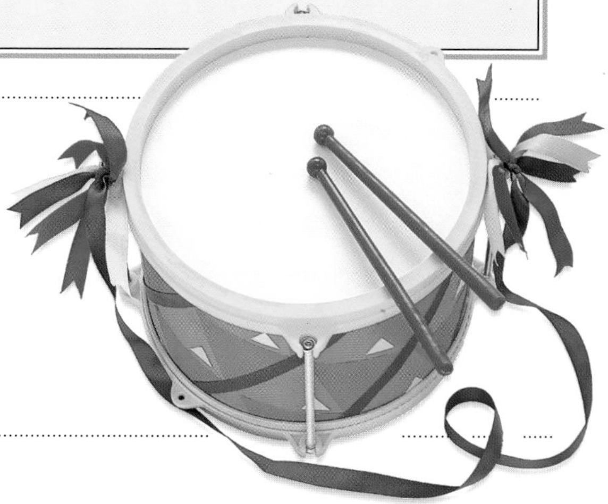

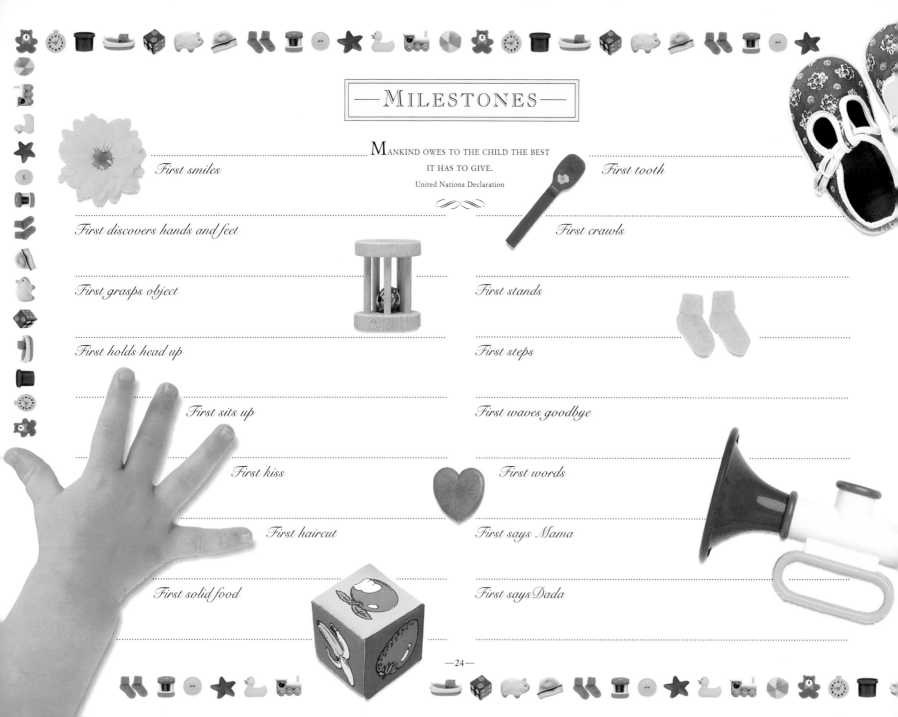

—MILESTONES—

Mankind owes to the child the best it has to give.

United Nations Declaration

First smiles ....

First discovers hands and feet ....

First grasps object ....

First holds head up ....

First sits up ....

First kiss ....

First haircut ....

First solid food ....

First tooth ....

First crawls ....

First stands ....

First steps ....

First waves goodbye ....

First words ....

First says Mama ....

First says Dada ....

W<small>E FIND DELIGHT IN THE BEAUTY AND</small>
<small>HAPPINESS OF CHILDREN THAT MAKES THE</small>
<small>HEART TOO BIG FOR THE BODY.</small>

Ralph Waldo Emerson

First recognizes:

Mother

Father

Grandparents

Special friends

Animals

First friends

PHOTOGRAPH

Notes

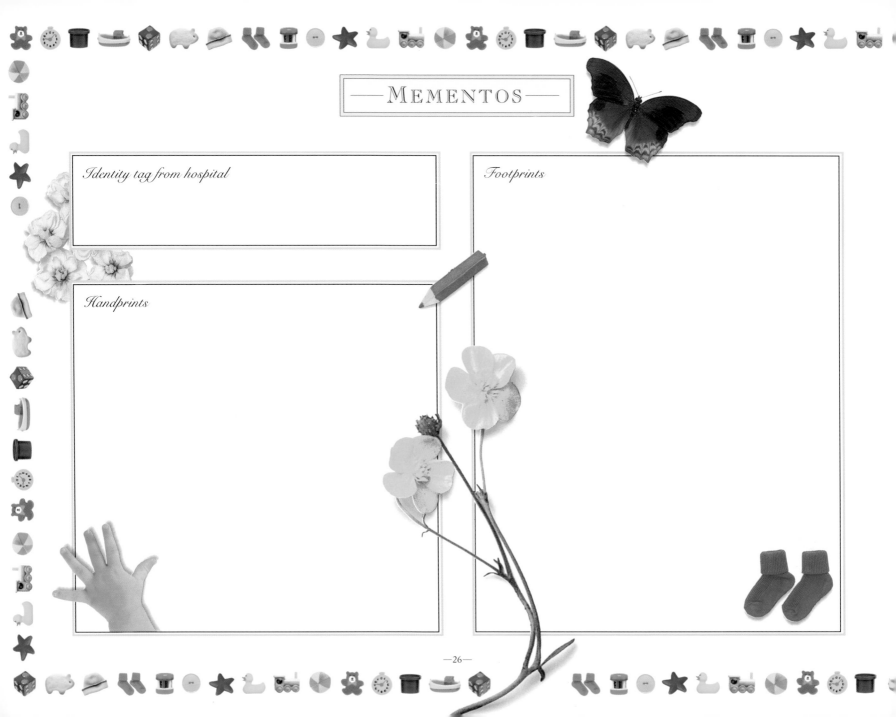

MEMENTOS

Identity tag from hospital

Footprints

Handprints

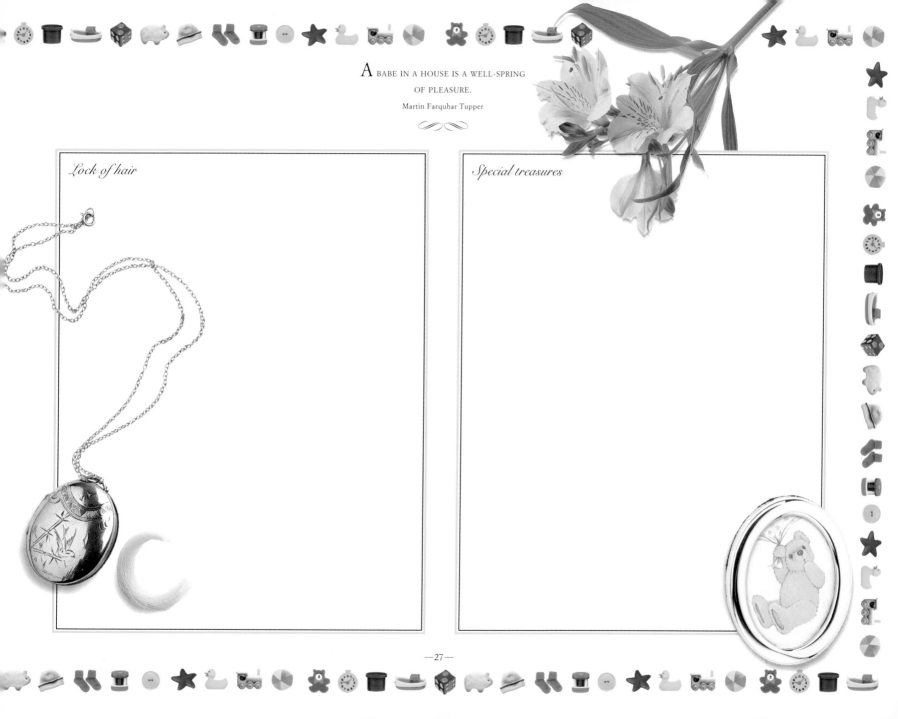

A BABE IN A HOUSE IS A WELL-SPRING
OF PLEASURE.

Martin Farquhar Tupper

Lock of hair

Special treasures

MEDICAL RECORD

THERE IS NO FINER INVESTMENT FOR ANY COMMUNITY THAN
PUTTING MILK INTO BABIES.

Winston Churchill

Immunization details

Vaccine	Age	Date
Diphtheria / Tetanus / Whooping Cough		
Polio		
Meningitis (Hib)		
Measles / Mumps / Rubella		
Other		

Illnesses

Diagnosis	Age	Date

Visits to doctor

Reason	Age	Date

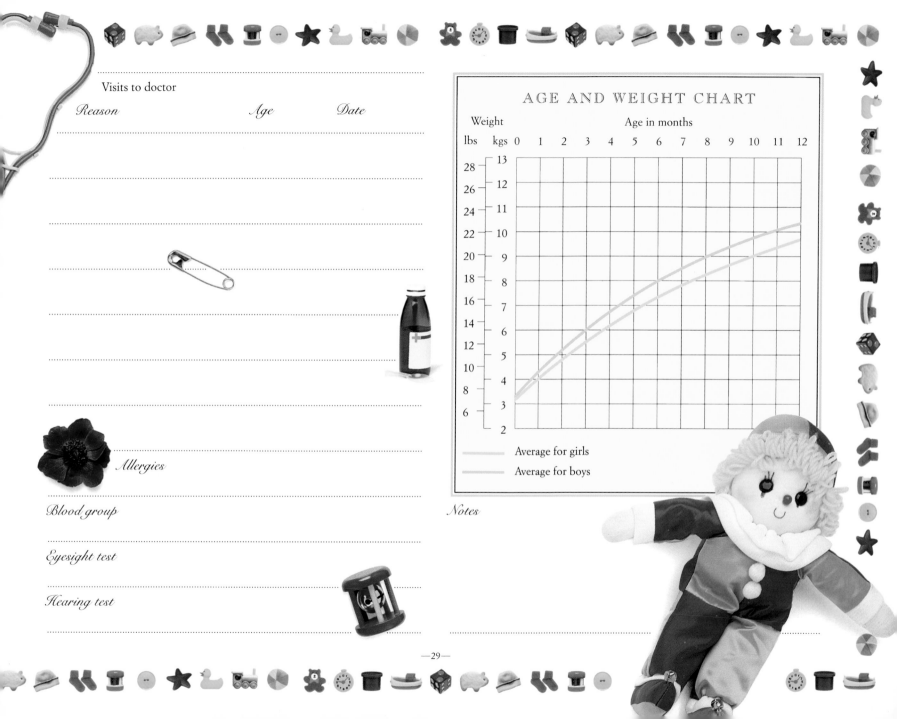

Allergies

Blood group

Eyesight test

Hearing test

AGE AND WEIGHT CHART

Weight   Age in months

lbs   kgs   0   1   2   3   4   5   6   7   8   9   10   11   12

28 — 13
— 12
26 —
24 — 11
— 10
22 —
20 — 9
— 8
18 —
16 — 7
— 6
14 —
12 — 5
— 4
10 —
8 — 3
6 — 2

———— Average for girls
———— Average for boys

Notes

— Special Memories —

Of all the wonderful things to have happened during your baby's first year of
life, some will stand out as particularly memorable and worth recording.

GIVE A LITTLE LOVE TO A CHILD, AND YOU
GET A GREAT DEAL BACK.

John Ruskin

Hopes for the Future

Plans for the future

Possible schools

Prediction of future occupation

Your baby's character

PERHAPS A CHILD WHO IS FUSSED OVER GETS A FEELING
OF DESTINY, HE THINKS HE IS IN THE WORLD FOR SOMETHING
IMPORTANT AND IT GIVES HIM DRIVE AND CONFIDENCE.

Benjamin Spock

PHOTOGRAPH

MONTH 1

FROM   TO
....

DAY 1	DAY 2	DAY 3	DAY 4		DAY 5	DAY 6
Date...........................						
DAY 7	DAY 8	DAY 9	DAY 10	DAY 11	DAY 12	DAY 13
DAY 14	DAY 15	DAY 16	DAY 17	DAY 18	DAY 19	DAY 20
DAY 21	DAY 22	DAY 23	DAY 24	DAY 25	DAY 26	
	DAY 27	DAY 28	DAY 29	DAY 30	DAY 31	

Don't forget – start using the stickers to record your baby's development

FROM .... TO ....

Weight ....

Length ....

Sleeping pattern ....
....

Bed time ....

Feeding pattern ....

Physical changes ....
....

Medical checks ....
....

New sounds ....
....

PHOTOGRAPH

Date of photograph ....

Response to mother ....

A typical day ....

Response to father ....

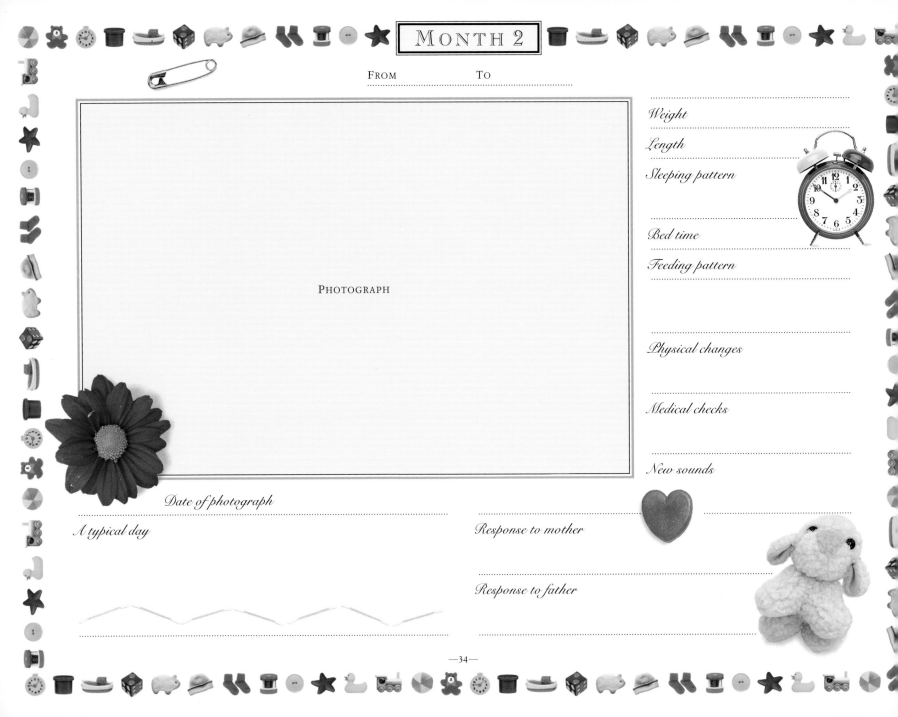

MONTH 2

FROM .... TO ....

PHOTOGRAPH

Weight ....

Length ....

Sleeping pattern ....

Bed time ....

Feeding pattern ....

....

Physical changes ....

....

Medical checks ....

....

New sounds ....

Date of photograph ....

A typical day ....

Response to mother ....

....

Response to father ....

....

FROM .... TO ....

DAY 1	DAY 2	DAY 3	DAY 4	DAY 5	DAY 6	DAY 7
Date						
DAY 8	DAY 9	DAY 10	DAY 11	DAY 12	DAY 13	DAY 14
DAY 15	DAY 16	DAY 17		DAY 18	DAY 19	DAY 20
DAY 21	DAY 22	DAY 23	DAY 24	DAY 25	DAY 26	
DAY 27	DAY 28	DAY 29	DAY 30	DAY 31		

MONTH 3

FROM .... TO ....

DAY 1	DAY 2	DAY 3	DAY 4	DAY 5	DAY 6	DAY 7
Date....................						
DAY 8	DAY 9		DAY 10	DAY 11	DAY 12	DAY 13
DAY 14	DAY 15	DAY 16	DAY 17	DAY 18	DAY 19	DAY 20
	DAY 21	DAY 22	DAY 23	DAY 24	DAY 25	DAY 26
	DAY 27	DAY 28	DAY 29	DAY 30	DAY 31	

FROM

TO

PHOTOGRAPH

Weight

Length

Sleeping pattern

Rises at

Bed time

Feeding pattern

Medical checks

Physical changes

New sounds

Response to mother

Response to father

A typical day

Date of photograph

FROM .... TO ....

Weight .... Length ....

Sleeping pattern ....

Rises at ....

Bed time ....

Description of meal time ....

Physical changes ....

New movements ....

New sounds ....

Medical checks ....

Favourite activities ....

A typical day ....

PHOTOGRAPH

Date of photograph

FROM   TO

....

DAY 1	DAY 2	DAY 3	DAY 4	DAY 5	DAY 6	DAY 7
Date						
DAY 8	DAY 9	DAY 10	DAY 11	DAY 12	DAY 13	DAY 14
	DAY 15	DAY 16		DAY 17	DAY 18	
DAY 19	DAY 20	DAY 21	DAY 22	DAY 23	DAY 24	
DAY 25	DAY 26	DAY 27	DAY 28	DAY 29	DAY 30	DAY 31

MONTH 5

FROM .... To ....

DAY 1	DAY 2	DAY 3	DAY 4	DAY 5	DAY 6	DAY 7
Date	DAY 8	DAY 9	DAY 10	DAY 11	DAY 12	DAY 13
	DAY 14	DAY 15	DAY 16	DAY 17		DAY 18
DAY 19	DAY 20	DAY 21	DAY 22	DAY 23		DAY 24
DAY 25	DAY 26	DAY 27	DAY 28	DAY 29	DAY 30	DAY 31

FROM .... TO ....

Weight ....

Length ....

Sleeping pattern ....

Rises at ....

Bed time ....

Description of meal time ....

Favourite foods ....

Medical checks ....

PHOTOGRAPH

Date of photograph ....

New movements ....

Favourite outing ....

Physical changes ....

A typical day ....

New sounds ....

Favourite activities ....

FROM   TO

PHOTOGRAPH

Weight

Length

Sleeping pattern

Rises at

Bed time

Description of meal time

Favourite foods

Medical checks

Date of photograph

Favourite outing

A typical day

New movements

Physical changes

New sounds

Favourite activities

FROM   TO

DAY
1

Date ....

DAY
2

DAY
3

DAY
4

DAY
5

DAY
6

DAY
7

DAY
8

DAY
9

DAY
10

DAY
11

DAY
12

DAY
13

DAY
14

DAY
15

DAY
16

DAY
17

DAY
18

DAY
19

DAY
20

DAY
21

DAY
22

DAY
23

DAY
24

DAY
25

DAY
26

DAY
27

DAY
28

DAY
29

DAY
30

DAY
31

MONTH 7

FROM .... TO ....

DAY 1	DAY 2	DAY 3	DAY 4	DAY 5	DAY 6	DAY 7
Date..........						
DAY 8	DAY 9	DAY 10			DAY 11	DAY 12
DAY 13	DAY 14	DAY 15	DAY 16	DAY 17	DAY 18	DAY 19
	DAY 20	DAY 21	DAY 22	DAY 23	DAY 24	DAY 25
	DAY 26	DAY 27	DAY 28	DAY 29	DAY 30	DAY 31

FROM .... TO ....

Weight ....

Length ....

Sleeping pattern ....

....

Rises at ....

Bed time ....

Description of meal time ....

Favourite foods ....

PHOTOGRAPH

Medical checks ....

Date of photograph ....

New movements ....

Favourite outing ....

Physical changes ....

A typical day ....

New sounds ....

Favourite activities ....

FROM .... TO ....

PHOTOGRAPH

Weight ....

Length ....

Sleeping pattern ....

....

Rises at ....

Bed time ....

Description of meal time ....

....

....

Favourite foods ....

....

Medical checks ....

Date of photograph ....

Favourite outing ....

A typical day ....

New movements ....

Physical changes ....

New sounds ....

Favourite activities ....

FROM   TO

DAY 1	DAY 2	DAY 3	DAY 4	DAY 5	DAY 6	DAY 7
Date						
DAY 8	DAY 9	DAY 10	DAY 11	DAY 12	DAY 13	DAY 14
DAY 15		DAY 16	DAY 17	DAY 18	DAY 19	DAY 20
DAY 21	DAY 22	DAY 23	DAY 24	DAY 25	DAY 26	
DAY 27	DAY 28	DAY 29	DAY 30	DAY 31		

MONTH 9

FROM .... TO ....

DAY 1	DAY 2	DAY 3	DAY 4	DAY 5		DAY 6
Date....................						
DAY 7	DAY 8	DAY 9	DAY 10	DAY 11	DAY 12	DAY 13
DAY 14	DAY 15	DAY 16	DAY 17	DAY 18	DAY 19	DAY 20
	DAY 21	DAY 22	DAY 23	DAY 24	DAY 25	
	DAY 26	DAY 27	DAY 28	DAY 29	DAY 30	DAY 31

Month 9

FROM .... TO ....

....

Weight .... Length ....

Sleeping pattern ....

....

Rises at ....

Bed time ....

Description of meal time ....

....

Physical changes ....

....

New movements ....

....

New sounds ....

....

Medical checks ....

Favourite activities ....

....

A typical day ....

....

PHOTOGRAPH

Date of photograph

MONTH 10

FROM .... TO ....

....

Weight .... Length ....

Sleeping pattern ....

....

....

Rises at ....

Bed time ....

Description of meal time ....

....

Physical changes ....

....

New movements ....

....

New sounds ....

....

Medical checks ....

Favourite activities ....

....

A typical day ....

....

PHOTOGRAPH

Date of photograph

FROM .... TO ....

DAY 1

Date ....

DAY 2

DAY 3

DAY 4

DAY 5

DAY 6

DAY 7

DAY 8

DAY 9

DAY 10

DAY 11

DAY 12

DAY 13

DAY 14

DAY 15

DAY 16

DAY 17

DAY 18

DAY 19

DAY 20

DAY 21

DAY 22

DAY 23

DAY 24

DAY 25

DAY 26

DAY 27

DAY 28

DAY 29

DAY 30

DAY 31

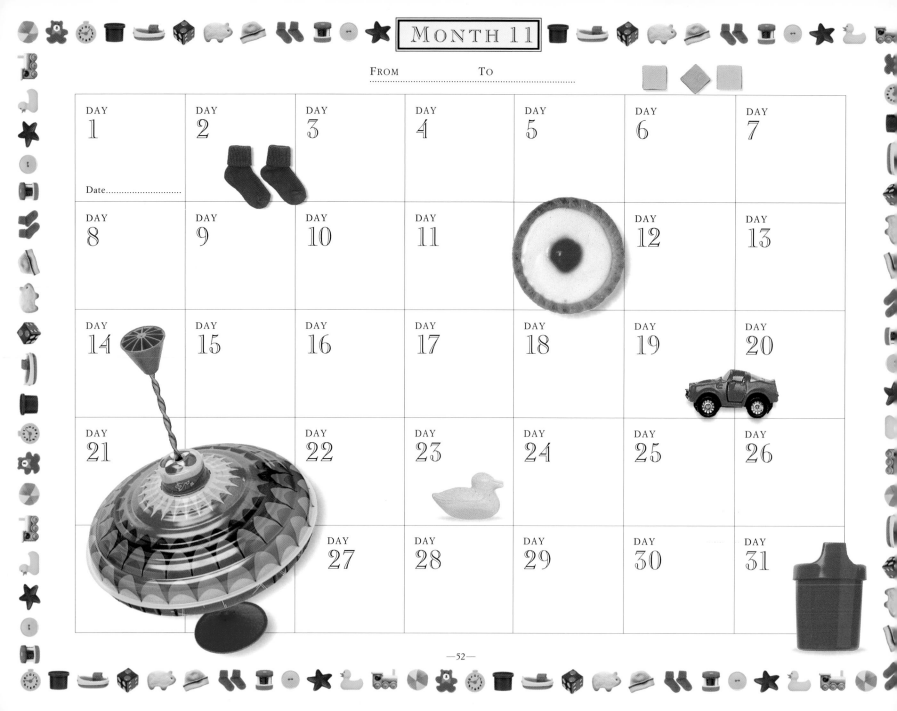

MONTH 11

FROM .... TO ....

DAY 1	DAY 2	DAY 3	DAY 4	DAY 5	DAY 6	DAY 7
Date...........................						

DAY 8	DAY 9	DAY 10	DAY 11		DAY 12	DAY 13

DAY 14	DAY 15	DAY 16	DAY 17	DAY 18	DAY 19	DAY 20

DAY 21	DAY 22	DAY 23	DAY 24	DAY 25	DAY 26

	DAY 27	DAY 28	DAY 29	DAY 30	DAY 31

FROM .... TO ....

Weight ....

Length ....

Sleeping pattern ....

....

Rises at ....

Bed time ....

Description of meal time ....

....

Favourite foods ....

....

Medical checks ....

PHOTOGRAPH

Date of photograph ....

New movements ....

Favourite outing ....

Physical changes ....

A typical day ....

New sounds ....

Favourite activities ....

FROM .... TO ....

PHOTOGRAPH

Weight ....

Length ....

Sleeping pattern ....

....

Rises at ....

Bed time ....

Description of meal time ....

....

Favourite foods ....

....

Medical checks ....

Date of photograph ....

Favourite outing ....

A typical day ....

New movements ....

Physical changes ....

New sounds ....

Favourite activities ....

MONTH 12

FROM .... TO ....

DAY 1	DAY 2	DAY 3	DAY 4	DAY 5	DAY 6
Date					
DAY 7	DAY 8	DAY 9	DAY 10	DAY 11	DAY 12	DAY 13
DAY 14	DAY 15		DAY 16	DAY 17	DAY 18	DAY 19
DAY 20	DAY 21	DAY 22	DAY 23	DAY 24		DAY 25
DAY 26	DAY 27	DAY 28	DAY 29	DAY 30		DAY 31

A Dorling Kindersley book
www.dk.com

Design Bernard Higton

Text Caroline Ash

Millennium edition published in 2000

First published in Great Britain in 1995 by
Dorling Kindersley Limited,
9 Henrietta Street, London WC2E 8PS

A CIP catalogue record for this book is available
from the British Library

ISBN 0 7513 0244 9

Colour reproduction by Colourscan, Singapore
Printed and bound in China by Imago

Photography: Stephen Oliver, Guy Ryecart,
Colin Keates Natural History Museum, DK Studio

*Dorling Kindersley would like to thank the following for their
kind permission to reproduce their photographs:*
Tony Stone: Martin Barraud p2/3

Baby RECORD BOOK STICKERS

HOMECOMING

FIRST SMILE

HOLDS HEAD UP

HOLDS OBJECT

SITS UP

FIRST BOTTLE

FIRST KISS

FIRST OUTING

FIRST HAIRCUT

FIRST NAIL TRIM

FIRST SOLID FOOD

USES BEAKER

EATS WITH SPOON

EATS AT TABLE

FIRST CRAWLS

FIRST TOOTH

FIRST BIG BATH

FIRST SLEEPS
THROUGH NIGHT

FIRST SLEEPS
IN COT

WAVES GOODBYE

FIRST WORD

FIRST PARTY

FIRST RELIGIOUS
CEREMONY

FIRST HOLIDAY

FIRST BABYSITTER

STANDS ALONE

FIRST STEPS

FIRST BIRTHDAY

FIRST VISIT TO
DOCTOR

VACCINATION

VACCINATION

VACCINATION

VACCINATION

VISIT TO DOCTOR

VISIT TO DOCTOR